2

3

4

Max grabbed the bag and ran off.

Woof, woof!

Tessa and Rocky ran after Max.

What was in the bag?

It was a snake!

The snake went away.

Max was not happy.
He did not wag his tail.

Mr Keeping looked for Tessa.

Tessa! Tessa!

Mr Keeping, Max grabbed the bag and ran off. We ran after Max, but we could not see him.

9

10

13